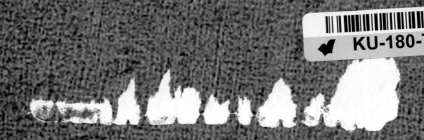

EDGAR ALLAN POE

Raintree is an imprint of Capstone Global Library Limited, a company incorporated in England
and Wales having its registered office at 7 Pilgrim Street, London, EC4V 6LB -- Registered
company number: 6695582

www.raintreepublishers.co.uk
myorders@raintreepublishers.co.uk

ISBN 978 1 406 26643 6
18 17 16 15 14 13
10 9 8 7 6 5 4 3 2 1

British Library Cataloguing in Publication Data
A full catalogue record for this book is available from the British Library.

Summary: The Usher mansion is in shambles and slowly sinking into the marsh
below. Its inhabitants are sickly and slipping into madness. Voracious ivy
creeps over the house. The wind whispers eerie omens. And the trees creak
as their branches reach out to greet its newest visitor...

Art Director: Bob Lentz
Graphic Designer: Hilary Wacholz
Edited by Diyan Leake
Production by Victoria Fitzgerald
Printed in China by Leo Paper Products Ltd

THE FALL OF THE HOUSE OF USHER

BY EDGAR ALLAN POE
RETOLD BY MATTHEW K. MANNING
ILLUSTRATED BY JIM JIMENZ

THERE WAS NO BACKING OUT OF IT.

NOT THAT I DIDN'T LOOK FOR A WAY. I DID MY VERY BEST, MIND YOU.

BUT RODERICK USHER WAS ONE OF THE FEW PEOPLE WHO HAD THE RATHER DUBIOUS HONOUR OF CALLING HIMSELF MY FRIEND.

AFTER ALL, RODERICK WASN'T ONE FOR MAKING NEW FRIENDS.

IT LOOKED DIFFERENT THAN I REMEMBERED.

THE HOUSE HAD NEVER BEEN A WELCOMING PLACE. BUT NOW IT WAS ALMOST IN RUINS.

AND IF RODERICK'S DESPERATE LETTER WAS ANY INDICATION...

I TOLD RODERICK I WOULD STAY AWHILE.

I DID MY BEST TO RAISE HIS SPIRITS.

SOME DAYS IT EVEN SEEMED TO WORK.

WE SPENT MOST OF THE TIME IN HIS SITTING ROOM, READING FROM HIS VAST COLLECTION OF BOOKS.

ALL THE WHILE, RODERICK WAS LIKE A JITTERY LITTLE PUPPY, CONSTANTLY NERVOUS AND ON EDGE.

WHILE MY COMPANIONSHIP DID SEEM TO HELP HIM A LITTLE...

...RODERICK'S SICKNESS WAS PROVING TO BE...

...INFECTIOUS.

OH, I'M SORRY. I DIDN'T KNOW YOU WERE STILL ASLEEP.

MADELINE HAS DIED.

OH, NO.

RODERICK, I'M SO SORRY.

I THINK WE SHOULD ENTOMB HER, DON'T YOU?

WAIT, WHAT DO YOU MEAN?

RODERICK WAS DISTRAUGHT. HIS MIND SEEMED UNTETHERED, FLOATING ABOUT RESTLESSLY.

RODERICK DECIDED TO PLACE MADELINE IN THE ABANDONED DUNGEONS BELOW THE ESTATE.

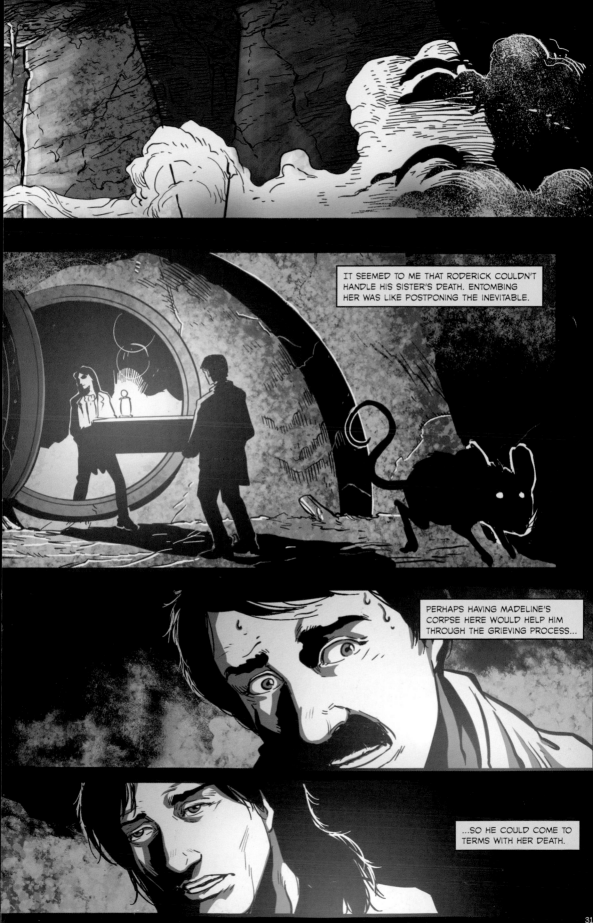

IT SEEMED TO ME THAT RODERICK COULDN'T HANDLE HIS SISTER'S DEATH. ENTOMBING HER WAS LIKE POSTPONING THE INEVITABLE.

PERHAPS HAVING MADELINE'S CORPSE HERE WOULD HELP HIM THROUGH THE GRIEVING PROCESS...

...SO HE COULD COME TO TERMS WITH HER DEATH.

34

THE FOLLOWING WEEK, RODERICK GOT WORSE.

WHAT WAS THAT?!

I DIDN'T HEAR ANYTHING.

I'D NEVER SEEN HIM THAT NERVOUS BEFORE.

I KNOW I HEARD SOMETHING.

THERE WAS NO REST FOR RODERICK THAT WEEK.

WOOSH!

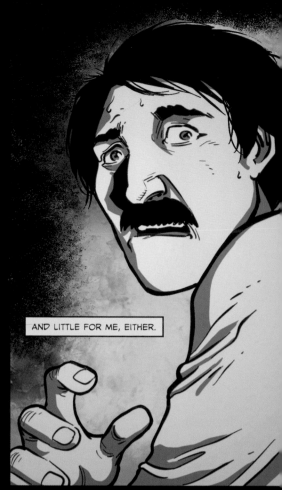

AND LITTLE FOR ME, EITHER.

I KEPT HEARING NOISES.

THUMP!

THUMP!

OOOOOOO

GASP!

RODERICK! YOU STARTLED ME.

I TAKE IT YOU CAN'T SLEEP EITHER?

"THE GOOD CHAMPION ETHELRED WAS DISAPPOINTED TO SEE NO SIGN OF THE EVIL HERMIT..."

"...BUT, INSTEAD OF THE HERMIT, A FIERCE DRAGON ROSE TO MEET ETHELRED."

"THAT WAS WHEN HE SAW THE MAGIC SHIELD ON THE WALL."

"THERE WAS AN INSCRIPTION ON THE SHIELD. IT READ:
'WHO ENTERETH HEREIN, A CONQUEROR HATH BIN;
WHO SLAYETH THE DRAGON, THE SHIELD HE SHALL WIN.'"

"ETHELRED CHARGED BRAVELY AT THE MENACING BEAST..."

"...EAGER TO CLAIM THE MAGIC SHIELD AS HIS PRIZE."

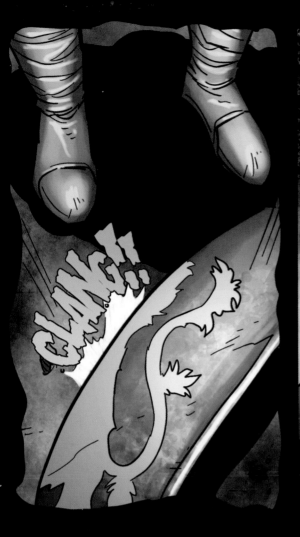

DID YOU HEAR THAT, RODERICK?!

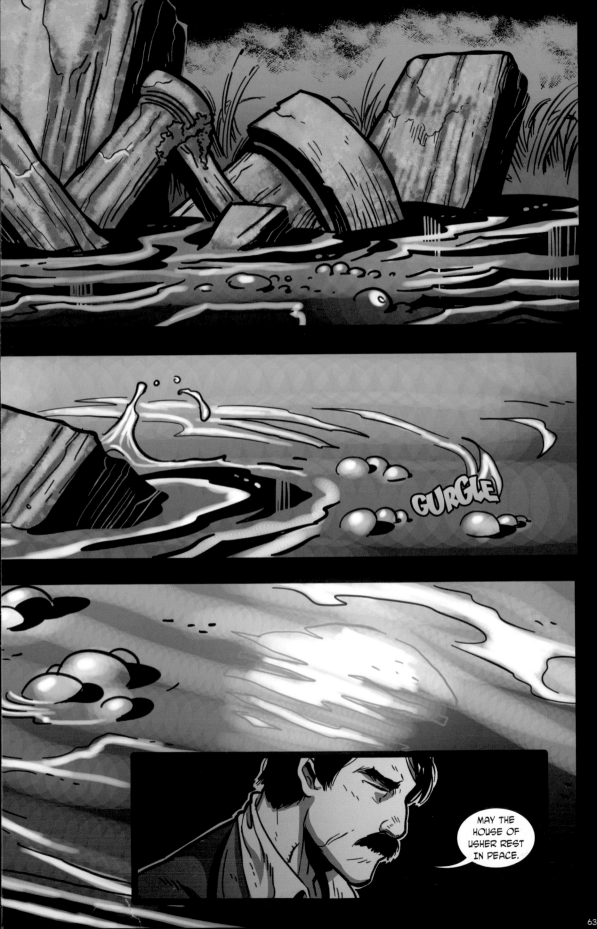

Over the course of his life, Edgar Allan Poe submitted many stories and poems to a number of publications. Either they were rejected, or he received little or no compensation for them. His most popular work, "The Raven", quite nearly made him a household name -- but only earned him nine dollars.

Poe was unable to hold a single job for very long, jumping from position to position for most of his life. He had very few friends, was in constant financial trouble, and struggled with alcoholism throughout his adult years. Edgar's family rarely helped him during these difficult times. In fact, when Edgar's father died in 1834, he did not even mention Edgar in his will.

Though largely unappreciated in his own lifetime, Edgar Allan Poe is now recognized as one of the most important writers of literature in English.

THE RETELLING AUTHOR

MATTHEW K. MANNING is a comic book writer, historian, and fan. Over the course of his career, he's written comics or books starring Batman, Superman, Iron Man, Wolverine, Captain America, Thor, Spider-Man, the Incredible Hulk, the Flash, the Legion of Super-Heroes, the Justice League, and even Bugs Bunny. Some of his more recent works include the hardcover for *The Batman Files* and an upcoming creator-owned, six-issue mini-series for DC Comics. He lives in Mystic, Connecticut, USA with his wife Dorothy and daughter Lillian.

THE ILLUSTRATOR

JIM JIMENZ is in a band with his brothers, Jay and Joy. Together, they have performed as the JBROTHERS for many years now. Jim's been a comic artist for even longer, working as an animator and layout artist for Walt Disney and Hanna Barbera.

GLOSSARY

CHAMPION fighter or warrior

COMPANIONSHIP the act of keeping a person company, or being a friend to someone

DISCORDANT harsh sounding, unpleasant to hear, or out of tune

DISTRAUGHT deeply agitated or crazy

DUBIOUS unsure or questionable

DWELLING place where someone or something lives, such as a house, apartment, or cave

ENTOMB bury or place in a tomb

GRIEVE feel very sad, usually because someone has died

HIDEOUS ugly or horrible

INFECTIOUS usually describes an illness that can spread easily from person to person

RESEMBLANCE similarity in appearance or likeness

SENTIENCE ability to sense or feel

VAST huge in area or extent

VISUAL QUESTIONS

1. The Usher family's house affects the people inside it. Identify a few points in this story where the house seems to be influencing its guests.

WHILE MY COMPANIONSHIP DID SEEM TO HELP HIM A LITTLE...

...RODERICK'S SICKNESS WAS PROVING TO BE...

...INFECTIOUS.

GRRRRAACK

2. This book has another story within it, *Mad Trist*, that features a brave knight and a fierce dragon. What does *Mad Trist* have in common with *The Fall of the House of Usher*? Why do you think *Mad Trist* was included in this book? Find a few places in the art where the two stories overlap.

3. Roderick Usher admits that he often thinks about whether or not plants are sentient, or can think. Identify a few points in this story where plants or nature affect the House of Usher or its inhabitants.

4. The name of the short story that inspired this book is called *The Fall of the House of Usher*. Why do you think Poe chose this title? There are a couple of ways in which the "House of Usher" in the title can be defined. Can you work out what they are?

5. Why do you think the house falls down when it does? Explain your answer using examples from the illustrations and the text.

THE MURDERS IN THE RUE MORGUE